PRACTICE EXERCISES IN BASIC
ENGLISH

Level C

Susan J. Riddle
Leslie K. Peters
Helen J. Cooper

*Illustrations by Ed Foxx
and Veronica Terrill
Cover Design by Ada Hanlon*

ISBN 0-8454-2628-1

 **CONTINENTAL PRESS**
Elizabethtown, PA 17022

CONTENTS

Write the letter that comes before each letter below in the alphabet.

___ d	___ m	___ u
___ h	___ q	___ w
___ k	___ s	___ y

Write the letter that comes after each letter below in the alphabet.

b ___	j ___	s ___
e ___	n ___	w ___
h ___	q ___	x ___

Alphabetical Order

a b c d e f g h i j k l m n o p q r s t u v w x y z

Alphabetical order is the order of the letters in the alphabet.

Write each group of letters below in alphabetical order.

c
b
a

1. _____

2. _____

3. _____

f
h
g

1. _____

2. _____

3. _____

l
k
n
m

1. _____

2. _____

3. _____

4. _____

u
w
v
t

1. _____

2. _____

3. _____

4. _____

Alphabetical Order

a b c d e f g h i j k l m n o p q r s t u v w x y z

Alphabetical order is the order of the letters in the alphabet.
We put words in alphabetical order by the first letter.

a comes before c

apple comes before cookie

Circle the letter and word that come first in alphabetical
order.

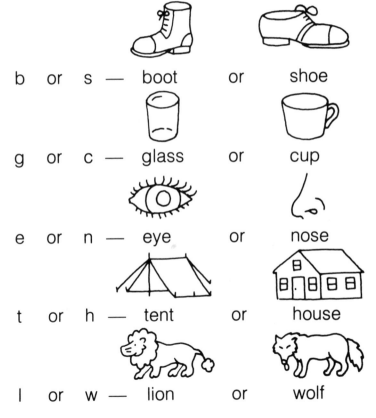

b or s — boot or shoe

g or c — glass or cup

e or n — eye or nose

t or h — tent or house

l or w — lion or wolf

Alphabetical Order   **5**

Alphabetical order is the order of the letters in the alphabet. We put words in alphabetical order by the first letter.

1. <u>b</u>asket
2. <u>c</u>ard
3. <u>f</u>ruit

Number each group of words in alphabetical order.

_____ owl

_____ deer

_____ tiger

_____ robin

_____ zoo

_____ park

_____ city

_____ farm

_____ father

_____ mother

_____ son

_____ uncle

_____ aunt

When words have the same first letter, we put them in alphabetical order by the second letter.

 star comes before sun

Write each group of words in alphabetical order.

clock
chair
candle

1. _____

2. _____

3. _____

elephant
ear
eye

1. _____

2. _____

3. _____

skate
snow
sled

1. _____

2. _____

3. _____

When words have the same first two letters, we put them in alphabetical order by the third letter.

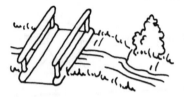

brook comes after bridge

Number each list of words in alphabetical order.

_____ boat

_____ boy

_____ book

_____ body

_____ bottle

_____ born

_____ drive

_____ dry

_____ dragon

_____ drum

_____ dream

_____ drop

We put names in alphabetical order by the first letter that is different.

1. Baker
2. M̲artinez
3. Mi̲tchell
4. Miy̲ata

Write these last names in alphabetical order.

Sanchez   Wilson   James
Johnson   Gray   Grimes
Greenberg   Arnold   West
              Monroe

1. _____   6. _____

2. _____   7. _____

3. _____   8. _____

4. _____   9. _____

5. _____   10. _____

Words are listed in a dictionary in alphabetical order.

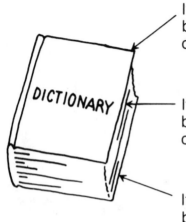

If you are looking for a word that begins with <u>A–G</u>, look in the <u>front</u> of a dictionary.

If you are looking for a word that begins with <u>H–P</u>, look in the <u>middle</u> of a dictionary.

If you are looking for a word that begins with <u>Q–Z</u>, look in the <u>back</u> of a dictionary.

Write <u>front</u>, <u>middle</u>, or <u>back</u> to tell where you would look for each word below in a dictionary.

1. dance _____

2. practice _____

3. tickle _____

4. world _____

5. breath _____

6. fresh _____

7. oven _____

8. rope _____

9. joy _____

10. quilt _____

Dictionary: Alphabetical Order

Words are listed in a dictionary in alphabetical order.

- •Words beginning with <u>A–G</u> are found in the <u>front</u> of a dictionary.
- •Words beginning with <u>H–P</u> are found in the <u>middle</u> of a dictionary.
- •Words beginning with <u>Q–Z</u> are found in the <u>back</u> of a dictionary.

Write each word from the box in the column below that tells where you would look for the word in a dictionary.

★ ★

knot	clue	gold	idea
vine	son	nest	act
east	hole	up	yard

★ ★

FRONT   MIDDLE   BACK

_____   _____   _____

_____   _____   _____

_____   _____   _____

_____   _____   _____

Dictionary: Alphabetical Order   **11**

Each page of a dictionary has <u>guide words</u> to help you find the word you are looking for.

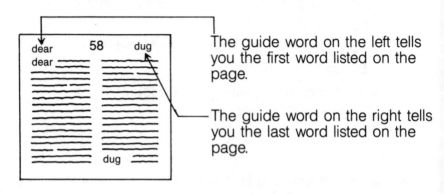

The guide word on the left tells you the first word listed on the page.

The guide word on the right tells you the last word listed on the page.

Words that come in alphabetical order after the first guide word and before the second guide word can be found on that page.

Write <u>yes</u> after each word below that would be found on the dictionary page shown above. Write <u>no</u> after each word that would not be on the page.

1. clay _____

2. doll _____

3. door _____

4. duck _____

5. ear _____

6. desk _____

7. dam _____

8. dust _____

9. dress _____

10. during _____

Dictionary: Guide Words

Each page of a dictionary has <u>guide</u> <u>words</u> to help you find the word you are looking for.

The guide word on the left tells you the first word listed on the page.

The guide word on the right tells you the last word listed on the page.

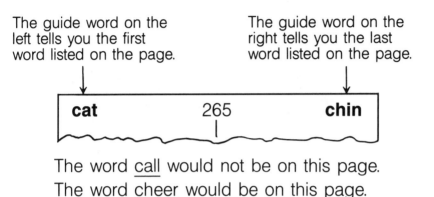

| cat | 265 | chin |

The word <u>call</u> would not be on this page.

The word <u>cheer</u> would be on this page.

Circle the words under each set of guide words below that would be found on that page of the dictionary.

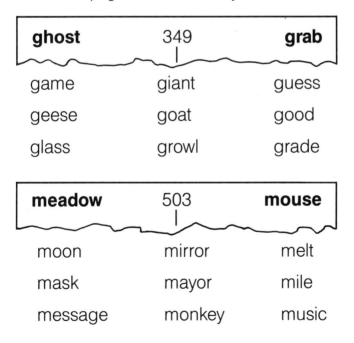

| ghost | 349 | grab |

game	giant	guess
geese	goat	good
glass	growl	grade

| meadow | 503 | mouse |

moon	mirror	melt
mask	mayor	mile
message	monkey	music

Nouns name people, animals, places, and things.

girl tiger office cloud

Circle two nouns in each sentence below.

1. My brother went to a party.
2. A clown did some tricks.

3. The car was parked in the garage.
4. The girl changed the flat tire.

5. A fox came out of the woods.
6. The chicken ran into the barn.

Nouns

Nouns name people, animals, places, and things. Nouns can name one or more than one.

one:	king	cat	bank	road
more:	kings	cats	banks	roads

Put a line under each noun that names one.
Put an X above each noun that names more than one.

1. Two farmers stood by the fence.

2. Cows were in the field.

3. The boy helped a calf.

4. Ducks swam in the pond.

5. Birds watched from the trees.

6. An airplane flew over the house.

We add -s to most nouns to make them name more than one.

truck

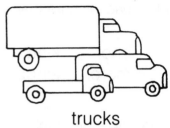

trucks

Write the noun given below the line + s to complete each sentence.

1. _____ are not real.
   Dragon

2. The _____ were hot.
   cookie

3. My _____ are empty.
   pocket

4. The _____ passed quickly.
   train

5. Two _____ flew high.
   kite

6. The _____ were ringing.
   bell

7. Hang up your _____.
   coat

Plural Forms: -s

We add -es to nouns that end in s, x, ch, or sh to make them name more than one.

glasses   foxes   lunches   bushes

Write a word from the box + es to name each picture below.

dish	brush	box
bus	dress	ranch
	watch	

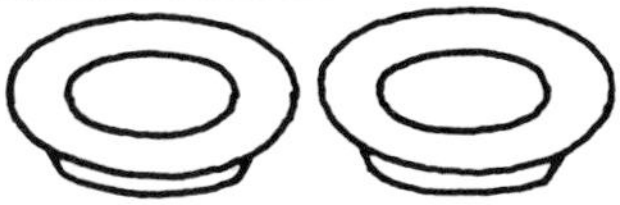

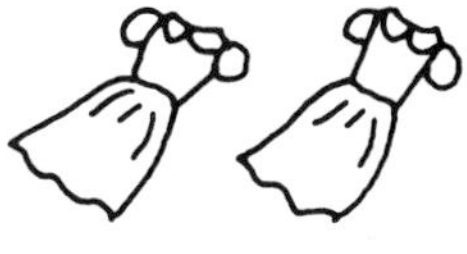

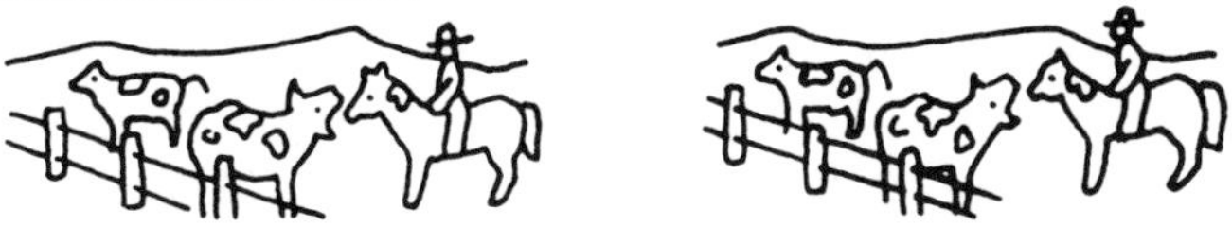

_____   _____

_____   _____

_____   _____

_____   _____

_____

We add -s to most nouns to make them name more than one. We add -es to nouns that end in s, x, ch, or sh to make them name more than one.

boot<u>s</u>   cross<u>es</u>

In the sentences below, add s or es to make the nouns name more than one.

1. Picnic____ inside can be fun.

2. Our neighbor____ came to eat.

3. The dish____ of food looked good.

4. Ann brought apple____.

5. Ron put the glass____ on the table.

6. We sat on large box____.

7. We should have more lunch____ like this!

Plural Forms: -s, -es

For each noun below, write the form that names more than one.

1. circle _____

2. grass _____

3. door _____

4. trunk _____

5. market _____

6. box _____

7. corner _____

8. bench _____

9. bell _____

10. brush _____

11. stove _____

12. class _____

Plural Forms: -s, -es

We change some nouns to make them name more than one.

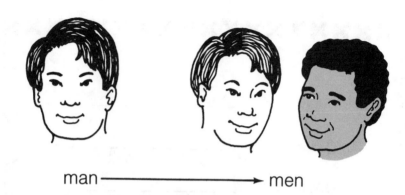

man ───────────────→ men

Draw a line from each noun that names one to the noun that names more than one of the same thing.

foot   teeth
child   women
woman   feet
tooth   children

Write one of the nouns above to complete each sentence.

1. All the _____ played in the park.

2. Did you lose a _____?

3. Put both _____ on the ladder.

4. My doctor is a _____.

We change some nouns to make them name more than one.

foot	tooth	man	woman	child
feet	teeth	men	women	children

Rewrite each sentence below. Change the underlined noun to make it name more than one.

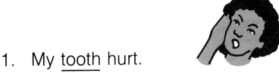

1. My <u>tooth</u> hurt.

_____

2. Some <u>man</u> talked.

_____

3. The <u>woman</u> worked hard.

_____

4. The <u>child</u> shouted.

_____

5. Tim stepped on my <u>foot</u>.

_____

Write <u>one</u> beside each noun that names one.
Write <u>more</u> beside each noun that names more than one.

1. bottles _____   9. ranches _____

2. seat _____   10. foot _____

3. cross _____   11. tent _____

4. rags _____   12. songs _____

5. jars _____   13. box _____

6. women _____   14. yard _____

7. gate _____   15. children _____

8. buses _____   16. wheels _____

Singular/Plural Review

Write the form that names more than one of the noun in ( ) to complete each sentence.

At the Park

1. I love _____ in the park.   (picnic)

2. We eat our _____ on the grass.   (lunch)

3. Mom made our _____.   (sandwich)

4. There is enough milk for two _____. (glass)

5. Then we take _____ on the slide.   (turn)

6. I push off with my _____ on the swing.   (foot)

7. We climb all over the monkey _____.   (bar)

8. _____ at the park are the best!
   (Afternoon)

Plural Forms Review   **23**

Action verbs tell what someone or something does or did.

grow   climb   live   bake

buy   make   visit

Write an action verb from the box to complete each sentence below.

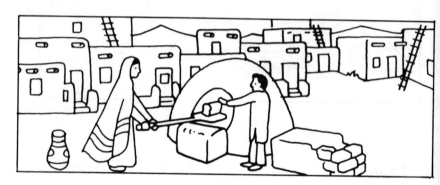

1. Some Native Americans _____ in Arizona.

2. They _____ ladders to their houses.

3. The Native Americans _____ corn.

4. The women _____ in large ovens.

5. They also _____ beautiful pots.

6. People _____ the Native Americans.

7. They often _____ the pots.

Action verbs have different forms.

Plain Form: The girls <u>swim</u> fast.
<u>s</u>-Form: Jay <u>swims</u> faster.

Write <u>P</u> after each plain form verb.
Write <u>S</u> after each <u>s</u>-form verb.

1. clap   ____

2. joins   ____

3. howl   ____

4. pushes   ____

5. finds   ____

6. stay   ____

7. travel   ____

8. prove   ____

9. hugs   ____

10. bites   ____

11. wander   ____

12. reach   ____

13. lift   ____

14. grows   ____

The plain form of a verb is used with nouns that name more than one.

Snails <u>move</u> slowly.

Write a plain form verb from the box to complete each sentence below.

fall   hunt   keep   lay
    help   sell   build

1. Stores _____ many things.

2. Beavers _____ dams.

3. Friends _____ each other.

4. Owls _____ at night.

5. Coats _____ us warm.

6. Leaves _____ from trees.

7. Hens _____ eggs.

The s-form of a verb is used with nouns that name one.

A spider <u>traps</u> flies.

Add <u>s</u> to each verb below to complete the sentences correctly.

1. Duffy collect____ shells.

2. That noise frighten____ me.

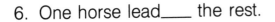

3. This cool drink taste____ good.

4. A snake crawl____ along.

5. Sometimes Ned strike____ out.

6. One horse lead____ the rest.

7. The hunter follow____ the tracks.

8. A bow shoot____ arrows.

s-Form

27

The plain form of a verb is used with nouns that name more than one.
The <u>s</u>-form of a verb is used with nouns that name one.

Skates <u>slide</u> on ice.
A sled <u>slides</u> on snow.

Circle the right verb form to complete each sentence correctly.

1. My sister write / writes me letters.

2. Logs float / floats in water.

3. A doctor take / takes care of us.

4. Flowers smell / smells good.

5. Cages hold / holds animals.

6. An owl sleep / sleeps in the day.

7. The twins wave / waves good-by.

Choose a verb form from the box to complete each
sentence correctly.

feed	bake	stand	fall
feeds	bakes	stands	falls
climb	give	belong	chase
climbs	gives	belongs	chases

1. A keeper _____ the lions.

2. Snow _____ in winter.

3. Cows _____ milk.

4. The cook _____ pies on Tuesday.

5. Some dogs _____ cats.

6. This book _____ to me.

7. Monkeys _____ trees.

8. The boys _____ straight.

The past form of a verb tells about something that has already happened. We add -ed to most verbs to make the past form.

 Last night I watched TV.

Add -ed to the verbs to make the sentences below tell about the past.

1. It rain____ on Saturday.

2. Jake want____ to see Bill.

3. He look____ up the number.

4. Then he call____ his friend.

5. Bill walk____ over.

6. The two boys play____ games.

7. Bill stay____ late.

Past Forms: -ed

We add -ed to most verbs to make the past form.

 This morning I open**ed** the mail.

Write the past form of the verb in ( ) to complete each sentence below.

1. Pat _____ in the garden.
   (work)

2. She _____ everything.
   (water)

3. She also _____ some new plants.
   (add)

4. Amy _____ the fence.
   (paint)

5. She _____ a few spots.
   (miss)

6. Pat _____ her where.
   (show)

For most verbs that end in <u>e</u>, we just add -<u>d</u> to make the past form.

chase ⟶ chase<u>d</u>

Add -<u>d</u> to the verbs to make the sentences tell about the past.

1. Luis like____ to cook.

2. He bake____ on Saturday.

3. He use____ good things in his cookies.

4. Luis hope____ they would turn out.

5. He whistle____ while he waited.

6. Everyone love____ the cookies.

7. They joke____ with Luis about them.

32   Past Forms: -*d*

We add -ed to most verbs to make the past form.
For most verbs that end in e, we just add -d.

walk → walk**ed**   dance → dance**d**

Write the past form of the verb in ( ) to complete each
sentence below.

(live)   1. The Willis family _____ in Chicago.

(move) 2. Then they _____ to New York.

(start)   3. Nan _____ school there.

(miss)   4. She _____ her old friends.

(follow) 5. One day a dog _____ her home.

(smile) 6. Nan _____ at her new pet.

(name) 7. She _____ it Happy.

Past Forms: -ed, -d   **33**

For some verbs, we change the verb itself to make the past form.

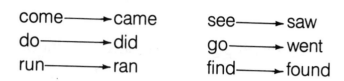

come ——→ came   see ——→ saw
do ——→ did   go ——→ went
run ——→ ran   find ——→ found

Circle the past form verb to complete each sentence below.

1. Nick _____ to the movies.
      go   went

2. He _____ a good picture.
      see   saw

3. Jenny _____ in a race.
        run   ran

4. She _____ in second.
      come   came

5. Ming _____ her work.
       do   did

6. She _____ the answers.
      find   found

Irregular Past Forms

For some verbs, we change the verb itself to make the past form.

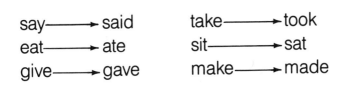

say ⟶ said   take ⟶ took
eat ⟶ ate   sit ⟶ sat
give ⟶ gave   make ⟶ made

Circle the past form verb to complete each sentence below.

1. Everyone _____ together.
   eat   ate

2. Jill _____ next to Beth.
   sit   sat

3. Juan _____ an airplane.
   make   made

4. He _____ it to the park.
   take   took

5. Dad _____ me a bike.
   give   gave

6. I _____ thank you.
   say   said

Irregular Past Forms   **35**

Write the past form of each verb.

1. run   _____

2. say   _____

3. find   _____

4. do   _____

5. give   _____

6. eat   _____

7. make   _____

8. go   _____

9. take   _____

10. see   _____

11. come   _____

12. sit   _____

Irregular Past Forms Review

Write the past form of the verb in ( ) to complete each sentence below.

(want)   1. The Kings _____ a tent.

(go)   2. They _____ to a nearby store.

(find)   3. They _____ many tents.

(like)   4. Mrs. King _____ the wall tent.

(see)   5. Dave _____ a pup tent.

(climb)   6. He _____ inside.

(wave)   7. Then he _____ .

Past Forms Review   **37**

We use nouns and verbs to make sentences.

Ducks   swim.

noun   verb

Complete the sentences.
Use the words in the Word Box below.

1. Telephones _____ .

2. Rabbits   _____ .

3. Kittens   _____ .

4. Cowhands _____ .

5. Dogs   _____ .

6. Cuts   _____ .

7. Squirrels   _____ .

WORD BOX			
purr	hurt	hop	howl
ring	ride	climb	red

In the sentence below, the noun is the <u>subject</u>. It names the person, animal, place, or thing the sentence tells about. The verb is the <u>predicate</u>. It tells what the subject is or was or does or did.

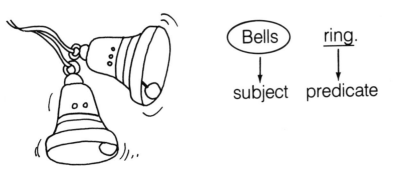

Circle the subject of each sentence.
Put a line under the predicate of each sentence.

1. Lions roar.

2. Roses bloom.

3. Lights flash.

4. Hands clap.

5. Balls bounce.

6. Crowds cheer.

7. Roosters crow.

The subject of a sentence tells whom or what the sentence is about. It is often more than one word and is usually the first part of a sentence.

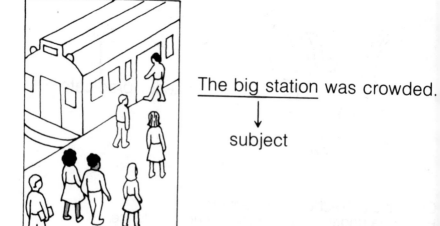

The big station was crowded.

↓

subject

Put a line under the subject of each sentence.

1. Everyone waited quietly.

2. A fast train pulled in at nine.

3. A few people got off.

4. Other people got on the train.

5. One family was going to Chicago.

6. Their long trip was just beginning.

7. The train left before ten.

Write a subject from the box to complete each sentence.

Some bees   All the books   The tiny airplane
The sun   The fastest boat   A big barn

1. _____ were in the library.

2. _____ won the race.

3. _____ landed quickly.

4. _____ make honey.

5. _____ burned down.

6. _____ came up early.

The Subject

The predicate of a sentence tells what the subject is or was or does or did. It is often more than one word and is usually the second part of a sentence.

The show <u>started at eight.</u>
↓
predicate

It <u>was exciting.</u>
↓
predicate

Put a line under the predicate of each sentence.

1. A singer came on first.

2. He sang a funny song.

3. A woman rode a horse.

4. She stood on its back.

5. The wild animals came next.

6. Tigers jumped through fire.

7. A man put his head in a lion's mouth.

The Predicate

Write a predicate from the box to complete each sentence.

fell all day	open early	pulled the cart
wagged its tail	smelled good	quacked loudly

1. The dog _____ .

2. The rain _____ .

3. The ducks _____ .

4. Dinner _____ .

5. An old horse _____ .

6. Many stores _____ .

The Predicate

The subject of a sentence tells whom or what the sentence is about.

The predicate of a sentence tells what the subject is or was or does or did.

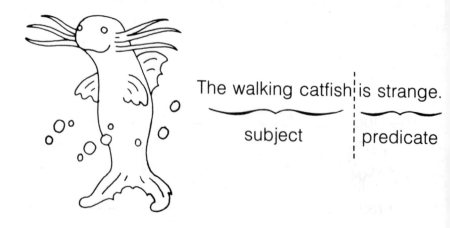

The walking catfish ¦ is strange.

subject ¦ predicate

Draw a line between the subject and the predicate of each sentence below.

1. This fish lives in ponds.

2. It crawls on land, too.

3. The fish moves from pond to pond.

4. Plants and animals are its food.

5. No animals kill this catfish.

6. Too many walking catfish hurt pond life.

7. People do not like them.

44

A sentence tells a complete thought. It has a subject and a predicate.

Anita.
  (not a sentence)

Went for the mail.
  (not a sentence)

Anita went for the mail.
  (a sentence)

Cross out each group of words that is not a sentence.

1. Many letters.

2. Anita gave them to her mother.

3. One card was for Anita.

4. Today is her birthday.

5. A large party.

6. The card was from her uncle.

7. Lives in Arizona.

8. Visits often.

Fragments

A sentence begins with a capital letter.

_People have always traveled.

Write the first word of each sentence below correctly.

1. _____ have been around a long time.
   cars

2. _____ first car was made in 1770.
   the

3. _____ man in France built it.
   a

4. _____ 1900, the first car show was held.
   in

5. _____ people went to see the cars.
   many

6. _____ cars are different.
   today

7. _____ have really changed.
   they

Capitalization: Sentences

Write a subject to complete each sentence. Be sure to begin each sentence with a capital letter.

1. _____
   scared all of us.

2. _____
   rolled down the hill.

3. _____
   shook the trees.

Write a predicate to complete each sentence.

1. The hungry wolf _____

   _____ .

2. A friendly neighbor _____

   _____ .

3. The people in the parade _____

   _____ .

Sentence Review   **47**

A sentence that tells ends with a period (.).
A sentence that asks ends with a question mark (?).

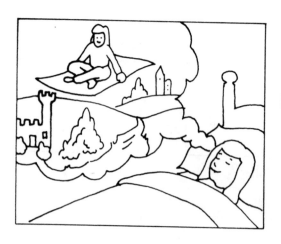

TELLS
Meg was sleeping.

ASKS
Did she dream?

Write T in front of each sentence that tells.
Write A in front of each sentence that asks.

_____ 1. Meg had a strange dream.

_____ 2. What was the dream?

_____ 3. She dreamed she flew through the air.

_____ 4. Where did she go?

_____ 5. What did she see?

_____ 6. It was a place Meg never saw before.

_____ 7. There were giant towers.

_____ 8. Was anyone else there?

Telling and Asking Sentences

A sentence that tells ends with a period (.).
A sentence that asks ends with a question mark (?).

TELLS	I like animals.
ASKS	What animal do you like best?

End each sentence below with a period (.) or a question mark (?).

1. I like raccoons best

2. What are raccoons like

3. Raccoons are small animals

4. Where do they live

5. They live in forests

6. Can they climb trees

7. What do they eat

8. Raccoons eat almost anything

End Punctuation

A sentence begins with a capital letter.
A telling sentence ends with a period (.).
An asking sentence ends with a question mark (?).

TELLS   It is after nine.

ASKS   Why are you late?

Cross out each small letter that should be a capital letter.
Write the capital letter above it.
End each sentence with a period or a question mark.

1. it has been a bad day

2. what happened

3. first, my brother couldn't get the car started

4. is that all

5. then we got a flat tire

6. could you fix it

7. another man stopped to help

50

Cross out each group of words below that is not a sentence.
Circle each small letter that should be a capital letter.
End each sentence with a period or a question mark.

1. heather's family has a small boat

2. do they use it much

3. they take it to the river

4. the bright sun

5. always rows

6. everyone has fun

7. can Heather swim

8. she likes swimming and fishing

Sentence Review

51

A sentence begins with a capital letter.
A telling sentence ends with a period (.).
An asking sentence ends with a question mark (?).

Long ago people planted corn by hand.
How is corn planted now?

Write each sentence correctly.

1. what country grows the most corn

_____

_____

2. there are many kinds of corn

_____

_____

3. popcorn is one kind

_____

4. is all corn yellow

_____

5. sweet corn is good to eat

_____

_____

The words in a sentence must be in a certain order to make sense.

Yes → We went to the baseball field.
No → To we baseball field the went.

Cross out each group of words below that is not in sentence order.

1. My friends play ball in the field.
2. Mother asked me to watch Ben.
3. My brother to go with me had.
4. I told Ben to sit on the grass.
5. Him find later could I not.
6. Home I all ran the way.
7. I was scared.
8. The steps Ben front on was sitting.

Word Order

The words in a sentence must be in a certain order to make sense.

Yes → Land turtles eat plants.
No → Plants land turtles eat.

Write each group of words in the correct order to make a sentence.

1. new Jerry shoes got.

_____

2. leg her broke Tina.

_____

3. music loud was The.

_____

4. not alone It's swim to safe.

_____

_____

5. rabbits the garden visited Hungry.

_____

_____

Word Order

The word order in an asking sentence is different from the word order in a telling sentence.

Tells → The soup was hot.
Asks → Was the soup hot?

Change the word order in each telling sentence to make an asking sentence.

1. The cookie jar is empty.

_____

_____

2. The sidewalk was covered with snow.

_____

_____

Change the word order in each asking sentence to make a telling sentence.

3. Are the stars out tonight?

_____

_____

4. Was the rocket ready?

_____

Some asking sentences begin with a question word. These are question words.

why   when   where   which
    how   what   who

Circle the best question word to begin each asking sentence.

1. _____ did you clean the bowl?
Who   When

2. _____ game was easiest?
Which   How

3. _____ let the cat out?
What   Who

4. _____ did Kim take it?
Where   Which

5. _____ did the bus stop?
Why   What

6. _____ day is Juana moving?
What   Who

7. _____ does a snake move?
Which   How

These are question words.

why   when   where   which

how   what   who

Write a question word to begin each asking sentence below. Remember that a sentence begins with a capital letter.

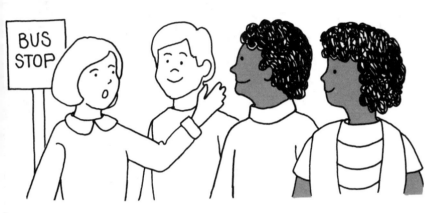

1. _____ is the train station?

2. _____ bus goes downtown?

3. _____ will it get here?

4. _____ time is it now?

5. _____ will I find you?

6. _____ can answer me?

7. _____ don't you come along?

We use <u>pronouns</u> in place of nouns. These pronouns can be used as subjects.

I   you   he   she   it   we   they

Circle each subject pronoun in the sentences below.

1. He rolled the ball to Mary.

2. She kicked the ball hard.

3. It went flying over the fence.

4. You should have seen that kick!

5. They all ran to get the ball.

6. We won the game.

7. I can't wait to play again.

58

We use <u>pronouns</u> in place of nouns. These pronouns can be used as objects. (An <u>object</u> answers what or whom after action verbs or words like <u>of</u>, <u>in</u>, <u>to</u>, <u>for</u>, <u>at</u>, <u>from</u>, <u>with</u>, <u>on</u>, and <u>by</u>.)

me   you   him   her   it   us   them

Circle each object pronoun in the sentences below.

1. Andy's friends visit him often.

2. Fran went sledding with them.

3. Ed's sled held all of us.

4. There is room enough for you.

5. Yumiko saw me when I fell.

6. Andy sent her for the sled.

7. Ed took it home.

Pronouns

We use I as a subject.
We use me as an object to answer what or whom after an action verb or a word like of, in, to, for, at, from, with, on, or by.

I wanted a camera.
Mom surprised me.
She bought it for me.

Write I or me to complete each sentence correctly.

1. _____ got the camera today.

2. Mom loaded it for _____ .

3. _____ wanted to take her picture.

4. Dad helped _____ .

5. _____ asked mom to smile.

6. Then _____ took the picture.

7. Later, dad took one of _____ .

8. My sister was splashing _____ .

60

Always name yourself last.

My brother and <u>I</u> cleaned the cellar.
Dad was proud of John and <u>me</u>.

Circle the right way to complete each sentence.

1. I and Joan
   Joan and I are twins.

2. Grandpa made breakfast for Bart and me
   me and Bart.

3. Mark and I washed the car.
   I and Mark

4. The squirrel ran away from me and Paula
   Paula and me.

5. I and my sister started a garden.
   My sister and I

6. Mom took me and Ellen to the zoo.
   Ellen and me

7. An old man yelled at Ken and me
   me and Ken.

We use <u>he</u> as a subject.
We use <u>him</u> as an object to answer what or whom after an action verb or a word like <u>of</u>, <u>in</u>, <u>to</u>, <u>for</u>, <u>at</u>, <u>from</u>, <u>with</u>, <u>on</u>, or <u>by</u>.

<u>He</u> forgot to bring lunch.

Kate watched <u>him</u>.

She felt sorry for <u>him</u>.

Write <u>he</u> or <u>him</u> to complete each sentence correctly.

1. A cat followed _____ .

2. _____ fed it.

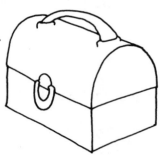

3. _____ named the cat Snowball.

4. Snowball is a good friend for _____ .

5. The cat is always with _____ .

6. Snowball loves _____ .

7. _____ gives Snowball a good home.

8. _____ would like to have other pets, too.

62

We use <u>she</u> as a subject.
We use <u>her</u> as an object to answer what or whom after an action verb or a word like <u>of</u>, <u>in</u>, <u>to</u>, <u>for</u>, <u>at</u>, <u>from</u>, <u>with</u>, <u>on</u>, or <u>by</u>.

<u>She</u> is Carl's cousin.

He met <u>her</u> at the station.

The trip seemed long to <u>her</u>.

Circle <u>she</u> or <u>her</u> to complete each sentence correctly.

1. Carl writes to she / her often.

2. She / Her will stay for a week.

3. Then Carl will visit she / her .

4. She / Her lives on a ranch.

5. Carl likes to go riding with she / her .

6. She / Her rides well.

7. She / Her has a cart, too.

8. The horse pulls she / her in it.

She/Her

We use <u>we</u> as a subject.
We use <u>us</u> as an object to answer what or whom after an action verb or a word like <u>of</u>, <u>in</u>, <u>to</u>, <u>for</u>, <u>at</u>, <u>from</u>, <u>with</u>, <u>on</u>, or <u>by</u>.

<u>We</u> won't get lost.

Street signs will help <u>us</u>.

The ride will be good for <u>us</u>.

Write <u>we</u> or <u>us</u> to complete each sentence correctly.

1. _____ went bike riding.

2. Dad came with _____ .

3. _____ rode carefully.

4. Cars passed _____ .

5. _____ walked across busy streets.

6. People waved to _____ .

7. Dogs barked at _____ .

8. _____ had a good time bike riding.

We use <u>they</u> as a subject.
We use <u>them</u> as an object to answer what or whom after an action verb or a word like <u>of</u>, <u>in</u>, <u>to</u>, <u>for</u>, <u>at</u>, <u>from</u>, <u>with</u>, <u>on</u>, or <u>by</u>.

<u>They</u> told Jan where to go.

She thanked <u>them</u>.

Then she walked away from <u>them</u>.

Circle <u>they</u> or <u>them</u> to complete each sentence correctly.

1. They / Them climbed the mountain.

2. They / Them were looking for berry bushes.

3. At last the boys saw they / them .

4. They / Them were full of berries.

5. The boys picked they / them .

6. They / Them carried their pails home.

7. Emmy made a pie for they / them .

8. She ate some of it with they / them .

They/Them

Circle the correct pronouns to complete the sentences.

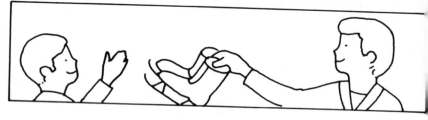

1. Jim's skates don't fit he / him .

2. They / Them are too small.

3. He / Him gave they / them to I / me .

4. That was nice of he / him .

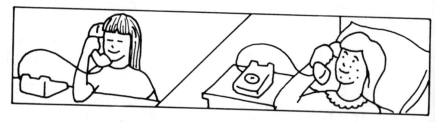

5. I / Me answered the telephone.

6. Sara was calling I / me .

7. She / Her was feeling better.

8. We / Us had sent cards to she / her .

9. Sara called to thank we / us .

I	you	he	she	it	we	they

me	you	him	her	it	us	them

Write a pronoun from one of the boxes to take the place of the word or words in ( ) under the sentences.

1. _____ helped _____ with the
   (Bob)   (Sue)
   work.

2. _____ will be leaving soon.
   (The visitors)

3. The truck driver waved to _____ .
                              (dad and me)

4. Sam ate all of _____ .
                   (the cookies)

5. Dean said to Peg, "Will _____ wait for
                            (Peg)

   _____?"
   (Dean)

6. _____ talked to _____ .
   (Val and I)   (Josh)

7. _____ returned _____ .
   (Nancy)   (the book)

Pronoun Review

An adjective tells something about a noun.

Gray Wolf was a <u>wise</u> man.

Circle the adjectives in the sentences below.

1. Native Americans lived in small villages.
2. They lived in long houses.
3. A few families lived together.
4. The proud men were good hunters.
5. Young women grew huge vegetables.
6. Brave boys ran long races.

An adjective tells something about a noun.
An adjective often comes before the noun it tells about.

<u>Busy</u> squirrels gather nuts.
<u>Clever</u> squirrels hide nuts.

Write an adjective from the box to complete each sentence below.

bad	dark	first	sunny	dirty	new

 1. I like _____ weather.

 2. My picture won _____ prize.

 3. Don't go in the _____ cave alone.

 4. Mrs. Bell had a _____ day.

 5. We have _____ neighbors.

 6. The _____ car needs washing.

Adjectives

69

Adjectives can also come after the nouns they tell about. They follow a <u>be</u> verb to tell something about the subject of the sentence.

The knife was <u>sharp</u>.

Write an adjective from the box to complete each sentence.

clean	flat	tall
loud	light	wrong

 1. The drums were _____ .

 2. This building is _____ .

 3. Feathers are _____ .

 4. The tire was _____ .

$2+3=6$ 5. This answer is _____ .

 6. My hands are _____ .

Adjectives

Rewrite each sentence. Add the adjective in () to tell something about a noun.

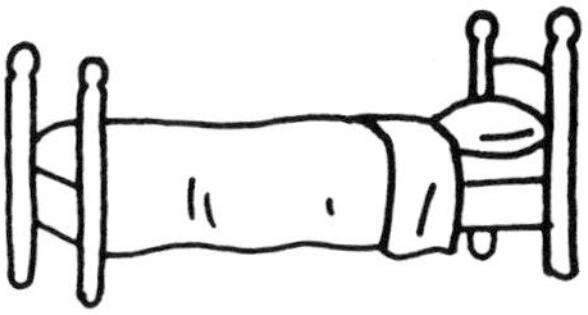

1. I have a bed. (soft)

_____

2. The woman shouted. (angry)

_____

3. The jet landed. (huge)

_____

4. We need a rope. (strong)

_____

5. Let's take a walk. (short)

_____

6. This is a story. (true)

_____

Adjectives

We use is with a subject that names one.
We use are with a subject that names more than one.
We use am with the pronoun I.

Malika is filling a pail.
We are digging.
I am working, too.

Circle is, are, or am to complete each sentence correctly.

     is
1. We are at the beach.
     am

       is
2. The sand are hot.
       am

  is
3. I are ready to swim.
  am

       is
4. The waves are fun.
       am

  is
5. I are getting a sunburn.
  am

   is
6. It are time to go home.
   am

72

We use <u>is</u> with a subject that names one.
We use <u>are</u> with a subject that names more than one.
We use <u>am</u> with the pronoun <u>I</u>.

This robin <u>is</u> building a nest.
Some birds <u>are</u> here all year.
I <u>am</u> looking for a blue jay.

Write <u>is</u>, <u>are</u>, or <u>am</u> to complete each sentence correctly.

1. I _____ a bird watcher.

2. Our yard _____ full of birds.

3. They _____ often singing.

4. Some songs _____ fighting songs.

5. One bird _____ eating.

6. Birds _____ afraid of noises.

7. I _____ very quiet.

Is/Are/Am

73

The past form of <u>is</u> is <u>was</u>. We use <u>was</u> with a subject that names one.
The past form of <u>are</u> is <u>were</u>. We use <u>were</u> with a subject that names more than one.

The line <u>was</u> full.

The shirts <u>were</u> dry.

Circle <u>was</u> or <u>were</u> to complete each sentence correctly.

1. Supper ^{was} / _{were} over.

2. The dishes ^{was} / _{were} dirty.

3. The moon ^{was} / _{were} out last night.

4. Some windows ^{was} / _{were} broken.

5. The girls ^{was} / _{were} playing.

6. My cat ^{was} / _{were} asleep.

7. The doctor ^{was} / _{were} friendly.

74

We use <u>was</u> with a subject that names one.
We use <u>were</u> with a subject that names more than one.

The coat <u>was</u> old.
Its buttons <u>were</u> missing.

Write <u>was</u> or <u>were</u> to complete each sentence correctly.

1. We _____ fishing last week.

2. The lake _____ crowded.

3. Holly _____ pointing.

4. Something _____ on Jack's line.

5. People _____ watching.

6. The children _____ excited.

7. A boot _____ caught on his hook!

8. We _____ laughing all the way home.

Was/Were

75

Rewrite these sentences. Use <u>was</u> in place of <u>is</u> and <u>were</u> in place of <u>are</u>.

1. The ice cream is melting.

_____

2. These are Jon's new glasses.

_____

3. A bird is chirping.

_____

4. My gloves are warm.

_____

5. Our car is clean.

_____

6. The rings are shiny.

_____

Forms of _Be_ Review

Write the correct word to complete each sentence.

1. I _____ going to the fair.
    am is are

2. The fair _____ open each night.
    is am are

3. The games _____ hard to win.
    is am are

4. My brother _____ coming in a while.
    is am are

5. Alex _____ here a year ago, too.
    were was

6. People _____ eating hot dogs.
    were was

7. I _____ sure I would win a prize.
    were was

8. The rides _____ all lots of fun.
    were was

Forms of *Be* Review

77

We can make a sentence say <u>no</u> by adding <u>not</u> after the verb.

Some cherries are sweet.
Some cherries are <u>not</u> sweet.

Rewrite these sentences. Add <u>not</u> after the verb to make them say <u>no</u>.

1. Sam is my brother.

_____

2. The bottles were empty.

_____

3. Carmen was late.

_____

4. I am sorry.

_____

5. Rabbits are good pets.

_____

Adding *Not*

A contraction is two words written together as one word with one or more letters left out. An apostrophe (') takes the place of the missing letter or letters. Many contractions are formed with the word <u>not</u>.

is not → isn't

are not → aren't

was not → wasn't

were not → weren't

Write the contraction for each pair of words in () to complete the sentences.

1. This plant _____ growing.
   (is not)

2. My answer _____ right.
   (was not)

3. The crows _____ frightened.
   (were not)

4. These shoes _____ mine.
   (are not)

5. Vicky _____ listening.
   (was not)

6. Some clowns _____ funny.
   (are not)

7. The bridge _____ finished.
   (is not)

Contractions

79

A contraction is two words written together as one word with one or more letters left out. An apostrophe (') takes the place of the missing letter or letters. Many contractions are formed with the word <u>not</u>.

do not → don∅t → don't

Draw a line from each pair of words to the contraction they form.

does not	couldn't
should not	doesn't
is not	haven't
were not	aren't
could not	shouldn't
has not	weren't
would not	wouldn't
have not	isn't
are not	hasn't

Contractions

Here are more contractions.

I am → I'm
I would → I'd
I will → I'll

he is → he's
she is → she's
it is → it's

we will → we'll

Write a contraction for each pair of words in () to complete the sentences.

1. _____ on Dick's team.
   (I am)

2. _____ our best runner.
   (He is)

3. _____ like to have a horse.
   (I would)

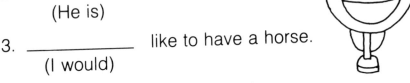

4. _____ fun to go riding.
   (It is)

5. _____ meet Leslie at the pool.
   (I will)

6. _____ bring Terry.
   (She will)

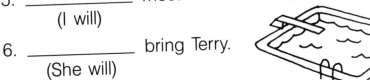

7. _____ go swimming.
   (We will)

Contractions

To make a noun that names one show ownership, we add 's.

A donkey's ears are long.

Add 's to the noun that should show ownership in each sentence.

1. The police officer____ whistle scared Evan.

2. Grace____ hair is long.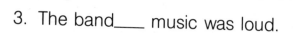

3. The band____ music was loud.

4. A king____ home is a castle.

5. The baby____ toys were on the floor.

6. The doctor____ bag was not in her office.

7. The rooster____ wings flapped wildly

8. I wrote with Tony____ pencil.

82

To make a noun that names one show ownership, we add **'s**.

the hat of a clown

a clown**'s** hat

Rewrite each phrase, using **'s** to show ownership.

1. the tail of a dog

_____

2. the truck my uncle owns

_____

3. the work of the farmer

_____

4. the bat of a player

_____

5. the bike Penny owns

_____

6. the paw of the bear

_____

Singular Possessive Forms

To make a noun that names more than one show ownership, we add an ' if the noun ends in s.

The twins' birthday is today.

Write the noun in () and an ' to complete each sentence correctly.

1. Our _____ cat ran up a tree.
      (neighbors)

2. Two of my _____ names are spelled alike.
      (friends)

3. The _____ team took first place.
      (girls)

4. Casey carried his _____ books.
      (sisters)

5. The _____ lunch starts soon.
      (teachers)

6. The _____ tests were finished.
      (scientists)

7. Where is the _____ meeting room?
      (doctors)

8. The _____ wagons were painted.
      (cowhands)

Plural Possessive Forms

To make a noun that names more than one show ownership, we add 's if the noun does not end in s.

the car of the policemen

the policemen's car

Rewrite each phrase, using 's to show ownership.

1. the prizes of women

_____

2. the toys of the children

_____

3. the meeting of the chairmen

_____

4. the ride of the horsewomen

_____

5. the tools of men

_____

6. the job of the saleswomen

_____

Plural Possessive Forms

To make a noun that names one show ownership, we add 's
To make a noun that names more than one show ownership,
we add an ' if the noun ends in s. If the noun does not end in
s, we add 's.

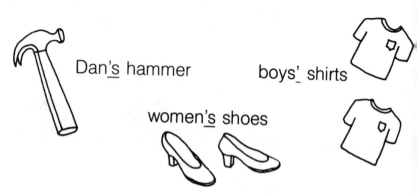

Dan's hammer   boys' shirts

women's shoes

Write the correct way to make each noun show ownership.

1. I could hear _____ voice in the hall.
                  Jennas'   Jenna's

2. The _____ whistles were loud.
       doormen's   doormens'

3. We like my _____ stories.
               mothers'   mother's

4. The _____ team is playing today.
       girls'   girls

5. That shop sells _____ games.
                  children's   childrens'

6. The _____ packs were heavy.
       explorers   explorers'

86

Add 's or an ' to each noun that should show ownership.

1. the lion trainer___ act

2. the doctors___ offices

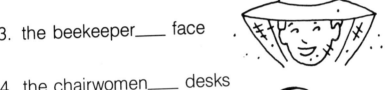

3. the beekeeper___ face

4. the chairwomen___ desks

5. a baby___ bed

6. Don___ garage

7. the hunters___ cabin

8. the workers___ tools

9. my neighbor___ car

10. the fishermen___ poles

Possessive Forms Review

Names of people begin with a capital letter.

Ray Hinton

Circle each small letter that should be a capital letter in these sentences.

1. My best friend is cindy patel.

2. kelly douglas is a new boy in school.

3. laurie hill drew a map to her house.

4. chita gomez came to our party.

5. Have you seen chip robinson?

6. phil gordon is a track star.

7. We played a game of tag with fred newman.

8. juan rivas is from Puerto Rico.

9. maureen grady took a picture of me.

10. The gift is for harry kennedy.

Capitalization: Names of People

An initial is the first letter of a name. It is a capital letter, and a period comes after it.

George Wong = <u>G</u>. <u>W</u>.

Write initials for the names below.

1. Wendy Brooks = _____

2. Henry Nakazawa = _____

3. Trish Lenska = _____

4. Barry Bergen = _____

5. Doug Hanson = _____

6. Tasha Rogers = _____

7. Eric Stein = _____

8. Felicia Ramirez = _____

Titles before names of people begin with a capital letter.

Mr.   Mrs.   Miss   Dr.

A period comes after Mr., Mrs., and Dr.

Write the titles in () correctly to complete each name.

1. _____ Rosa Martino lives in apartment B.
   (mrs)

2. Our teacher is _____ Paul Boyer.
   (mr)

3. _____ Helen Painter fixed my arm.
   (dr)

4. The letter was from _____ Nancy Fry.
   (miss)

5. _____ Gary Stone moved to New York.
   (dr)

6. _____ Lois Curtis spoke at the meeting.
   (mrs)

7. The picture was done by _____ Lee Chung.
   (mr)

8. _____ Clara Gustav is my aunt.
   (miss)

Names of people and their titles begin with a capital letter.
Initials are capital letters.
Names of pets also begin with a capital letter.

Dr. J. B. Ames is an animal doctor.

Gail took her bird Singer to him.

Circle each small letter that should be a capital letter.

1. Mom works for mr. ramon garcia.

2. The police found my dog sunny.

3. Tonight miss irene horner will sing.

4. mrs. brenda short has a cat named callie.

5. dr. roger t. beam was late.

6. tammy named her fish goldy.

7. We asked mrs. mary e. king to dinner.

8. Who was dr. george w. carver?

Capitalization: Names of People and Pets

Names of the days of the week begin with a capital letter.

Sunday   Tuesday   Friday
Monday   Wednesday   Saturday
                Thursday

Write the name of the day correctly to complete each sentence.

1. Banks are closed on _____.
                                sunday

2. Last _____ Gene found a dollar.
            thursday

3. We made cookies on _____.
                                tuesday

4. The best shows are on _____.
                                saturday

5. Eva didn't go to school on _____.
                                        friday

6. Where were you on _____?
                            monday

7. The circus opened _____.
                            wednesday

Capitalization: Days

Names of months begin with a capital letter.

January	May	September
February	June	October
March	July	November
April	August	December

Circle each small letter that should be a capital letter in these sentences.

1. january and february are the first two months of the year.

2. In march and april there are signs of spring.

3. Cookouts are fun in may and june.

4. july and august are good months for swimming.

5. The air is cool in september and october.

6. Stores are crowded in november and december.

Names of holidays begin with a capital letter.

Halloween

Christmas

Thanksgiving

Labor Day

Hanukkah

New Year's Day

Easter

Write the name of a holiday to complete each sentence correctly.

1. We light eight candles for _____.

2. The first day of January is _____.

3. Alicia has a funny mask for _____.

4. Let's have a picnic on _____.

5. We ate pumpkin pie on _____.

6. Rick wants a sled for _____.

7. There will be an egg hunt on _____.

94

Names of days, months, and holidays begin with a capital letter.
Circle each small letter that should be a capital letter in the sentences below.

1. This year independence day is on friday.

2. Grandmother came for a visit on tuesday.

3. We haven't seen her since memorial day.

4. We were ready for the parade by thursday.

5. There will be a big picnic on sunday.

6. The month of august always seems to go fast.

7. The end of summer comes on labor day.

8. We go back to school in september.

Capitalization Review

Names of streets begin with a capital letter.

Maple Avenue   Beach Road
First Street   Lake Drive

Write the name of each street correctly.

1. pine drive   _____

2. park road   _____

3. front street _____

4. elm avenue   _____

5. grant street _____

6. kings road   _____

7. third avenue _____

8. center drive _____

Names of cities, towns, states, and countries begin with a
capital letter.

Boston   Cedar Falls   Georgia
                        United States

Circle each small letter that should be a capital letter in the
sentences below.

1. Abe Lincoln was born in kentucky.

2. Later his family moved to indiana.

3. In 1831, Abe lived in illinois.

4. He worked in a store in new salem.

5. Abe lived in springfield for many years.

6. He became president of the united states.

7. His last home was in washington.

Capitalization: Names of Places

The first word and all important words in the title of a book begin with a capital letter.

 <u>R</u>iding a <u>T</u>rain

Write a title from the box correctly to complete each sentence.

to the moon and back   pak of korea
bat and ball   riding herd
growing flowers   easy cooking

1. _____ tells how to fix wonderful dinners.

2. I read about spaceships in

   _____ .

3. _____ has stories and pictures of cowhands.

4. Learn about gardens in

   _____ .

5. _____ tells about a boy in another country.

6. If you like baseball, read _____ .

In the sentences below, cross out each small letter that should be a capital letter. Write the capital letter above it.

1. Our dog tiny barks at squirrels.

2. We always have fun on halloween.

3. My uncle likes to fish in canada.

4. mrs. g. t. sandstone lives in utah.

5. The apartment building is on front street.

6. School is over on friday.

7. Hakim's birthday is in september.

8. Have you ever been to miami?

9. looking for dragons tells stories about long ago.

Capitalization Review

All the sentences in a paragraph should tell about one thing or idea.

Early homes in our country were made of logs. ~~My house is made of bricks.~~ Most log houses had only one room and a dirt floor.

Cross out the sentences that do not belong in each paragraph below.

There is a tree in our yard. Long ago it was hard to travel. In many places there were no roads. Then trees were cut down to make roads. Trees take a long time to grow.

Whistling swans live in North America. They are beautiful birds. I have a parrot named Silver. Now they are disappearing. Can your bird talk? There are only a few hundred of them left.

All the sentences in a paragraph should tell about one thing or idea.

We begin the first sentence of a paragraph in from the left margin.

→There are many kinds of houses. Some are large and some are small. There are also very old ones as well as new ones.

Rewrite the following group of sentences in paragraph form. Leave out the two sentences that do not belong. Be sure to begin the first sentence of the paragraph in from the left margin.

Many city people live in apartments. Their buildings may be many stories high. I like to read stories. In the country, houses are farther apart. People often have to go a long way to visit each other. Toby's dad works in a bank.

_____

_____

_____

_____

_____

_____

The sentences in a paragraph should be in the right order. Number the sentences below in the right order to tell a story about the pictures. Then write the sentences in paragraph form.

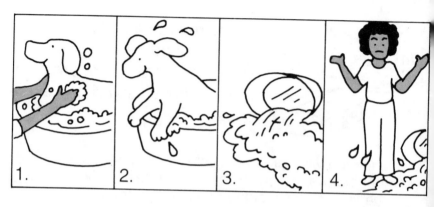

—— He kept jumping out of the tub.

—— Yesterday I gave Frisky a bath.

—— I think he gave me the bath!

—— The water splashed everywhere.

All the sentences in a paragraph should tell about one thing or idea. The sentences should also be in the right order. Read the sentences below. Cross out the two sentences that do not belong. Write the rest of the sentences in the right order to make a paragraph that tells about the pictures.

Mrs. Brown saw smoke over the roof of our house. The Smith family lives next door. The fire fighters found meat burning on the fire. Most fires start in the home. She quickly called the firehouse.

A friendly letter has five parts.

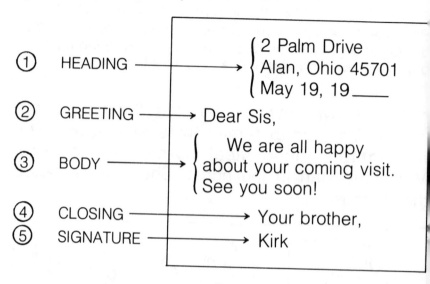

① HEADING → 2 Palm Drive
Alan, Ohio 45701
May 19, 19____

② GREETING → Dear Sis,

③ BODY → We are all happy about your coming visit. See you soon!

④ CLOSING → Your brother,

⑤ SIGNATURE → Kirk

Write the name of each part of the friendly letter below.

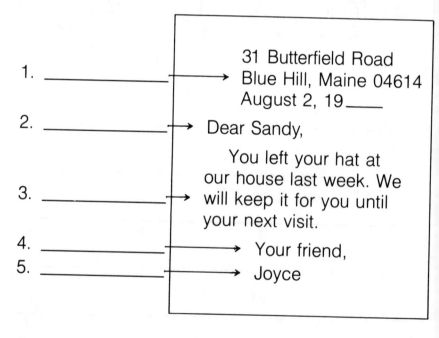

1. _____ → 31 Butterfield Road
Blue Hill, Maine 04614
August 2, 19____

2. _____ → Dear Sandy,

3. _____ → You left your hat at our house last week. We will keep it for you until your next visit.

4. _____ → Your friend,

5. _____ → Joyce

104

A friendly letter has five parts.

1. The HEADING tells the address of the writer and the date the letter is written. The names of places and the name of the month begin with a capital letter.
2. The GREETING says "hello." The first word and the name begin with a capital letter.
3. The BODY is what the letter has to say. The first word of every sentence begins with a capital letter.
4. The CLOSING says "good-by." The first word begins with a capital letter.
5. The SIGNATURE is the writer's name. It begins with a capital letter.

Circle each small letter that should be a capital letter in the letter below.

44 apple avenue
moose, wyoming 83012
march 25, 19 ____

dear hank,

   i hope you are feeling better by now. we all miss you at school.

     your friend,
     pete

In a friendly letter, we use a comma (,)
- in the HEADING between the name of the city and the name of the state. There is also a comma between the day and the year in the date.
- after the GREETING.
- after the CLOSING.

Circle the commas in the letter below.

306 Lemon Street
Hope, Michigan 48628
October 17, 19_____

Dear Elena,

    Ricardo told me that your story won first prize. We are all proud of you. Write soon.

                Your cousin,
                Nita

Place commas correctly in the letter below.

2191 Sun Drive
Redkey Indiana 47373
February 5 19_____

Dear Tony

    I am sending you some books I have read. I hope that you enjoy them.

                Your friend
                Sharon

Writing Friendly Letters

We write thank-you letters when people give us presents.
You should name the present and tell something about it.

26 Cook Road
Nampa, Idaho 83651
August 30, 19____

Dear Aunt Marian,

names the present → Thank you for the scarf.
It came the day before
tells something → yesterday. It will look perfect
about the present with my new fall coat.

Love,
Chris

Will's friend Candy gave him a baseball glove for his birthday.
Write the body of this thank-you letter from Will to Candy.

96 Cactus Avenue
Eloy, Arizona 85231
April 7, 19____

Dear Candy,

_____

_____

_____

Your pal,
Will

An invitation should tell <u>what</u>, <u>where</u>, and <u>when</u>.

17 Adams Road
Forest, Virginia 24551
September 29, 19 ___

Dear Mother,

what
where
when

Please come to the class play
in Room 5 at 2 o'clock on Friday.

Love,
Marty

Joanne has two tickets to the circus in Dallas for next
Saturday at 3 o'clock. She wants to ask Steve to go with her
to see the show. Write the body of Joanne's invitation.

922 Wells Avenue
Dallas, Texas 75267
June 10, 19 ___

Dear Steve,

_____

_____

_____

_____

Your friend,
Joanne

Write a letter to a friend in the space below. Use your
address in the heading and your name in the signature.

We put two addresses on an envelope. One shows who is to get the letter. The other shows who is sending the letter.
In an address, the names of people and places begin with a capital letter. There is a comma between the name of the city and the name of the state.

From ⟶ Mr. Luke Perry
601 Third Street
Soldier, Kansas 66540

To ⟶ Dr. Ruth T. Sill
42 Hill Drive
Coats, Kansas 67028

In each address below, circle each small letter that should be a capital letter. Put a comma between the name of the city and the name of the state.

mrs. barbara ross
1426 green street
fairfield kentucky 40020

miss kendra hutton
53 fox road
market oregon 97420

Envelopes

We often use abbreviations in addresses. An abbreviation is a short way to write a word. A period comes after it.

N. = North   S. = South   E. = East   W. = West
    St. = Street   Ave. = Avenue
R.D. = Rural Delivery   Apt. = Apartment

Put a period after each abbreviation in the addresses below.

Mr. Sid Young
17 N First St
Burns, Colorado 80426

Mrs. Ann Young
R D 1
Camp, Arkansas 72520

Miss Marta Diaz
339 W Brook Road
Apt 4
Newport, New Jersey 08345

Dr. Cliff Freeman
27 S Garden Ave
Walker, South Dakota 57659

We often use abbreviations in addresses. An abbreviation is a short way to write a word. The post office has set up abbreviations for the names of all the states. They are capital letters and are not followed by periods.

North Dakota = ND   Maine = ME

Draw a line from the name of each state to the abbreviation that stands for it.

Pennsylvania	NY
California	DE
New York	MT
Montana	CA
Florida	OK
Oklahoma	PA
Delaware	IL
Georgia	TN
Hawaii	FL
Illinois	WA
Tennessee	HI
Washington	GA

Envelopes

In the addresses below, cross out each small letter that should be a capital letter. Write the capital letter above it. Put commas and periods where they belong.

miss gina cook

563 e high st

lakewood ny 14750

mrs louise case

r d 3

drums pa 18222

mr greg low

44 s river ave

cook wa 98605

miss eileen wang

15 sandy road

apt 7B

parker fl 32401

Synonyms are words that have the same, or almost the same, meaning.

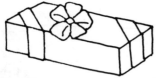 gift or present

Draw a line from each word on the left to its synonym on the right.

brook	ocean
sea	cent
allow	shut
penny	stream
beautiful	woods
close	let
road	pretty
forest	street

Synonyms are words that have the same, or almost the same, meaning.

large or huge

Complete the sentences below by writing a synonym from the box for each word in ( ).

tiny	scared	fast	began	smiled
	glad		shouted	

Tim and I heard a strange sound. We both

_____ at the same time. At first we were
(yelled)

_____. We wanted to get away _____.
(frightened)   (quickly)

Then we _____ to look around. We saw a
(started)

_____ animal behind a can. Tim _____.
(little)   (grinned)

We were _____ it was nothing dangerous.
(happy)

Antonyms are words that have opposite meanings.

heavy   light

Draw a line from each word on the left to its antonym on the right.

happy   dirty

wet   right

clean   dry

far   old

same   sad

young   low

wrong   different

high   near

Antonyms are words that have opposite meanings.

     empty   full

Complete the sentences below by writing an antonym from the box for each word in ( ).

kind	late	found	bad
	start	remember	push

Yesterday Dad was _____ for work. He
(early)

had some _____ luck. He couldn't get the
(good)

car to _____. A _____ man
(stop)   (mean)

helped him. They tried to _____ the car.
(pull)

Finally they _____ the trouble. Dad did
(lost)

not _____ to buy gas!
(forget)

Antonyms

117

Homophones are words that sound alike but are spelled differently and have different meanings.

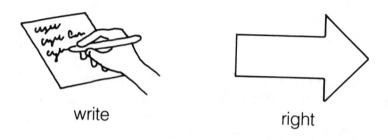

write   right

Draw a line to join each pair of homophones.

would	by
hear	wood
ate	road
buy	eight
knew	through
rode	here
dear	new
threw	deer

Homophones are words that sound alike but are spelled differently and have different meanings.

Debbie brought <u>two</u> cakes <u>to</u> the party.
Roy brought some food, <u>too</u>.

<u>Two</u> means "the number 2."
<u>To</u> means "toward."
<u>Too</u> means "also."

Write <u>two</u>, <u>to</u>, or <u>too</u> to complete each sentence below correctly.

1. We went _____ the boat race.

2. The race started at _____ o'clock.

3. _____ boats were far ahead.

4. A small boat was near them, _____.

5. But it turned back _____ shore.

6. One large boat sailed _____ the finish line.

7. The other boat finished, _____.

Homophones

Homophones are words that sound alike but are spelled differently and have different meanings.

Their plans are to get there early.

Their means "belonging to them."
There means "in that place."

Write their or there to complete each sentence below correctly.

1. _____ cat had kittens.

2. Four of them are _____ in the box.

3. _____ eyes are still shut.

4. Two of them look like _____ mother.

5. The two white ones and two black ones are out

   _____ in the hall.

6. They sleep over _____.

7. _____ cries keep everyone awake.

Homophones

Circle the right word to complete each sentence below.

Last summer our family went ___ the mountains.
                                    to   too

At noon we stopped ___ the side of the ___. The
                              by   buy   rode   road

picnic tables were _____. We _____ our lunch. I could
                              their   there   eight   ate

_____ something moving. Suddenly we saw ___ black
here   hear   too   two

bears. They wanted to eat _____ lunch, ___. We
                                        their   there   to   too

_____ it was dangerous to eat _____.
knew   new   there   their

We use <u>a</u> before words that begin with a consonant sound.
We use <u>an</u> before words that begin with a vowel sound.

<u>a</u> lion   <u>an</u> ostrich

Circle <u>a</u> or <u>an</u> to complete each sentence correctly.

1. Kevin lives in ___ apartment.
           a an

2. Last night he was looking out ___ open window.
           a an

3. He saw ___ falling star.
      a an

4. Kevin made ___ wish.
      a an

5. He would like to take ___ interesting trip.
        a an

6. He dreams of flying ___ airplane to ___ island far
        a an   a an

   away.

7. Someday he'll find ___ way to make his dream
        a an

   come true.

122

We use <u>a</u> before words that begin with a consonant sound.
We use <u>an</u> before words that begin with a vowel sound.

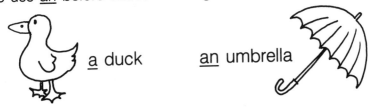

<u>a</u> duck   <u>an</u> umbrella

Write <u>a</u> or <u>an</u> to complete each sentence below correctly.

In 1937, _____ Oklahoma City man had _____

idea. Sylvan Goldman thought of _____ easy way for

people to shop. He invented _____ shopping cart.

The cart had _____ basket and _____ folding seat.

There was also _____ place under the basket for

large things.

Mr. Goldman was _____ clever man. He knew

that _____ empty cart would help people buy more.

A/An   **123**

Has and have are words that can help to tell about the past.
We use has with subjects that name one.
We use have with subjects that name more than one.

Bonnie has cleaned the car.
Her brothers have washed the windows.

Write has or have to complete each sentence correctly.

1. Jeff _____ gone to a baseball game.
   have   has

2. His friends _____ joined him there.
   have   has

3. Each one _____ bought a cap.
   have   has

4. They _____ talked about the players.
   have   has

5. This program shows the team _____ won 63
   have   has
   games.

6. We _____ rooted for this team for a long time.
   have   has

7. Pat said "Going to this game _____ been fun."
   have   has

Helping Words

We use <u>saw</u> alone to tell about the past.
We use <u>seen</u> with helping words like <u>has</u> or <u>have</u>.

Liza <u>saw</u> a parade today.
I have <u>seen</u> it, too.

Write <u>saw</u> or <u>seen</u> to complete each sentence correctly.

1. We have _____ the Rose Parade.
        seen   saw

2. First we _____ the bands march by.
        seen   saw

3. You should have _____ the huge floats.
        seen   saw

4. We _____ one ten feet high.
        seen   saw

5. We also have _____ some beautiful horses and
        seen   saw
their riders.

6. Liza has _____ the parade before.
        seen   saw

7. She _____ it on TV last year.
        seen   saw

8. But I never _____ it until now.
        seen   saw

Irregular Verb Forms

We use <u>did</u> alone to tell about the past.
We use <u>done</u> with helping words like <u>has</u> or <u>have</u>.

Brad <u>did</u> the work.
He <u>has</u> <u>done</u> all he can.

Write <u>did</u> or <u>done</u> to complete each sentence correctly.

1. Brad is proud of the painting he has _____ .

2. He _____ most of the painting himself.

3. Sometimes he has _____ it with help from

friends.

4. They have _____ barns and houses.

5. They have _____ doghouses.

6. Yesterday they _____ something new.

7. They _____ a neighbor's fence.

8. They _____ it very well.

126

We use these words alone to tell about the past.

came	went	gave
ran	ate	took

We use these words with helping words like <u>have</u> or <u>has</u>.

come	gone	given
run	eaten	taken

Write the correct word to complete each sentence below.

1. Long ago buffalo _____ free.
   ran   run

2. Native Americans killed some and _____ them.
   eaten   ate

3. They also _____ the buffalo skins.
   took   taken

4. Many of the buffalo have _____ now.
   went   gone

5. But today people have _____ these animals
   gave   given

   another chance.

6. Parks have been set up, and there buffalo have

   _____ again.
   ran   run

7. Each year people have _____ to see the herds.
   come   came

Irregular Verb Forms

Write the correct verb form to complete the second sentence in each pair.

1. Abby <u>did</u> a perfect eight on the ice.

    She has _____ other tricks, too.

2. Mr. Greene always <u>took</u> people around.

    He has _____ a lot of people in his bus.

3. I <u>ate</u> dinner at Jose's place.

    It's the first time I have _____ there.

4. Irma's dog <u>has</u> <u>run</u> away.

    But it _____ back to her when she called.

5. The moving truck <u>came</u> to our house.

    Aunt Julia has _____ to help us pack.

6. I <u>saw</u> a man take off in a spaceship.

    He has _____ the earth from the moon.

7. Chad <u>went</u> to the park.

    Sarah has _____ to find him.

8. Mom <u>has</u> <u>given</u> me some money.

    I _____ part of it to my brother.

Irregular Verb Form Review